Session Skills
for Drums
Initial-Grade 2

Published by
Trinity College London
www.trinitycollege.com

Registered in England
Company no. 02683033
Charity no. 1014792

Printed in England by Caligraving Ltd.
Written, recorded and produced by Camden Music Services.
Exercises devised by George Double, backing tracks by Tom Fleming.

SESSION SKILLS

CONTENTS

SESSION SKILLS

INTRODUCTION

To be a great rock and pop musician you need to develop a range of important musical skills – from performing with flair to improvising and picking up new songs quickly. Trinity College London's Rock & Pop exams are designed to help you develop these skills and take your musicianship to the next level.

An important part of each Rock & Pop exam is the **session skills** test. For this you can choose either **playback** or **improvising**:

- ⚡ **Playback** involves playing some music you have not seen or heard before, testing your ability to pick up new musical material quickly

- ⚡ **Improvising** involves performing an improvisation over a backing track, testing your ability to respond creatively to a specified musical style and chord sequence.

About this book

This book is specially designed to help you prepare for the session skills test at Initial to Grade 2, whether you choose playback or improvising. It contains plenty of example tests to use for practice, as well as a CD of backing tracks. It also includes specific guidance on how to approach playback and improvising at Initial, Grade 1 and Grade 2.

Please note that Rock & Pop exams require you to perform three songs as well as the session skills test. A range of songs for each grade level are provided in a separate series of Rock & Pop song books, also published by Trinity. Additional songs can be downloaded at www.trinityrock.com, where you can also find the syllabus and a range of resources for teaching and learning. The syllabus can change from time to time, so check the website regularly to make sure you are referring to an up-to-date version.

SESSION SKILLS

THE TESTS

Playback

If you choose playback for the session skills test, you'll be asked to perform some music you have not seen or heard before. You'll be given a song chart and 30 seconds to study it and try out any sections. The examiner will then play the backing track.

You should listen to the backing track, playing back what you hear and reading the music from the song chart if you want. You'll hear a series of short phrases – you should repeat each of these straight back in turn. A count-in will be given at the beginning of the backing track, and a backing click will play throughout.

In the exam you'll have two chances to play along with the backing track: first time for practice and second time for assessment. If you choose to read the music from the song chart, remember that for each repeated phrase you should listen the first time and play the second time.

Improvising

If you choose improvising for the session skills test, you'll be asked to improvise in a specific style over a backing track you have not heard before. You'll be given a chord chart, and the examiner will play a short section of the backing track to give you a feel for the tempo and style. You'll have 30 seconds to study the chord chart and try out any sections. The examiner will then play the backing track.

You should improvise in the specified style over the backing track, which will consist of four repetitions of the chord sequence shown on the chord chart. A count-in will be given at the beginning of the backing track, and a backing rhythm will play throughout.

In the exam you'll have two chances to play along with the backing track: first time for practice and second time for assessment. A count-in will be given both times.

SESSION SKILLS

PARAMETERS

Trinity provides a full set of parameters for the session skills tests. Published online at www.trinityrock.com, these tell you which musical elements are featured in improvising and playback at each grade. All the example tests in this book have been written to fit with these parameters, so you can be sure that the test in the exam will be similar to the examples in this book.

The following is a summary of the parameters for Initial to Grade 2. Visit www.trinityrock.com for the full set of parameters across all grades.

Playback

For drummers at Initial to Grade 2, playback is always eight bars long. Within this, each phrase is two bars long, making a total of four phrases. At Initial and Grade 1 the time signature can be $\frac{2}{4}$ or $\frac{4}{4}$, and at Grade 2 it can also be $\frac{3}{4}$.

You can expect to see minims (half notes), crotchets (quarter notes) and quavers (eighth notes) in playback at Initial and Grade 1, with some crotchet and minim rests. At Grade 2 there can also be dotted minims and ties.

No dynamics feature at Initial, but p and f are used at Grade 1 and 2, so to try to observe these dynamics where they appear. At Grade 2 there can also be accents.

Improvising

For drummers at Initial to Grade 2, the chord sequence is always four bars long with one chord per bar. The backing track consists of four repetitions of this sequence, requiring an improvisation that lasts 16 bars in total. The time signature is always $\frac{4}{4}$ at Initial and Grade 1. At Grade 2 it can also be $\frac{3}{4}$.

Improvising at Initial is in either simple rock or pop style. At Grade 1 it can also be in ballad or heavy rock style, with country style appearing at Grade 2.

INITIAL   PLAYBACK

Example 1

Example 2

Example 3

Example 4

> ⚡ **TOP TIP** Remember that to perform the playback test you can read from the song chart or copy what you hear by listening to the backing track - or both. It's up to you and there is no right or wrong way of doing it.

Example 5

Example 6

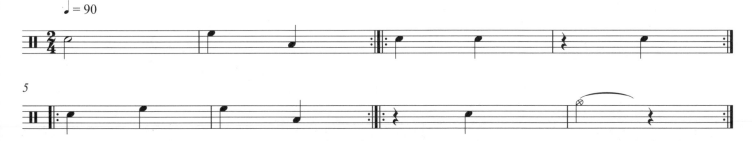

INITIAL   IMPROVISING

Example 1

TRACK 11

♩ = 100 **Simple Rock**

| Am | Em | Dm | Am |

Example 2

TRACK 12

♩ = 96 **Simple Rock**

| Em | Am | Em | Am |

Example 3

TRACK 13

♩ = 80 **Pop**

| C | G | C | F |

Example 4

TRACK 14

♩ = 84 **Simple Rock**

| G | G | D | C |

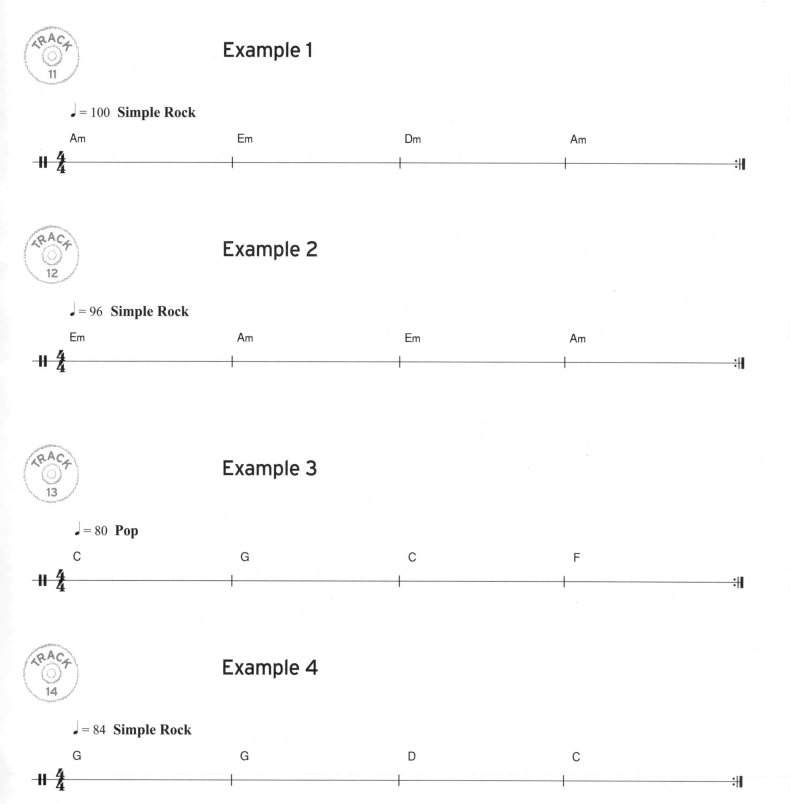

TRACK 15

Example 5

♩ = 100 **Pop**

| Am | Am | Em | Dm |

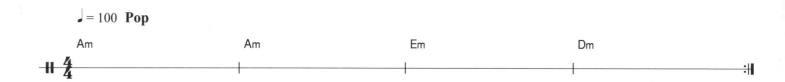

TOP TIP The backing track consists of four repetitions of the chord sequence, giving you the chance to do different things in your improvisation on each repeat. Think about how you could vary your improvisation over the four repetitions.

TRACK 16

Example 6

♩ = 108 **Pop**

| Am | Em | Em | Am |

TRACK 17

Example 7

♩ = 100 **Simple Rock**

| Em | Em | Am | Em |

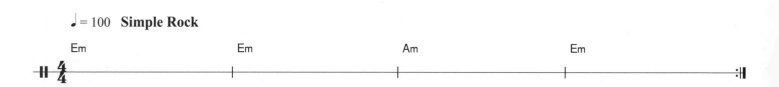

Example 8

♩ = 80 **Pop**

| D | G | G | A |

Example 9

♩ = 84 **Pop**

| G | C | D | D |

TOP TIP You don't have to fill your whole improvisation with sound - remember that you can also use rests, or silences. Can you practise using rests in your improvisations to make some effective contrasts with the sound of the drums?

Example 10

♩ = 120 **Simple Rock**

| C | C | F | G |

GRADE 1 PLAYBACK

Example 1

Example 4

TOP TIP Notice that dynamics have been introduced into playback at Grade 1. Take care to observe these to create some effective musical contrasts.

Example 5

Example 6

Example 7

Example 8

Example 9

Example 10

GRADE 1   IMPROVISING

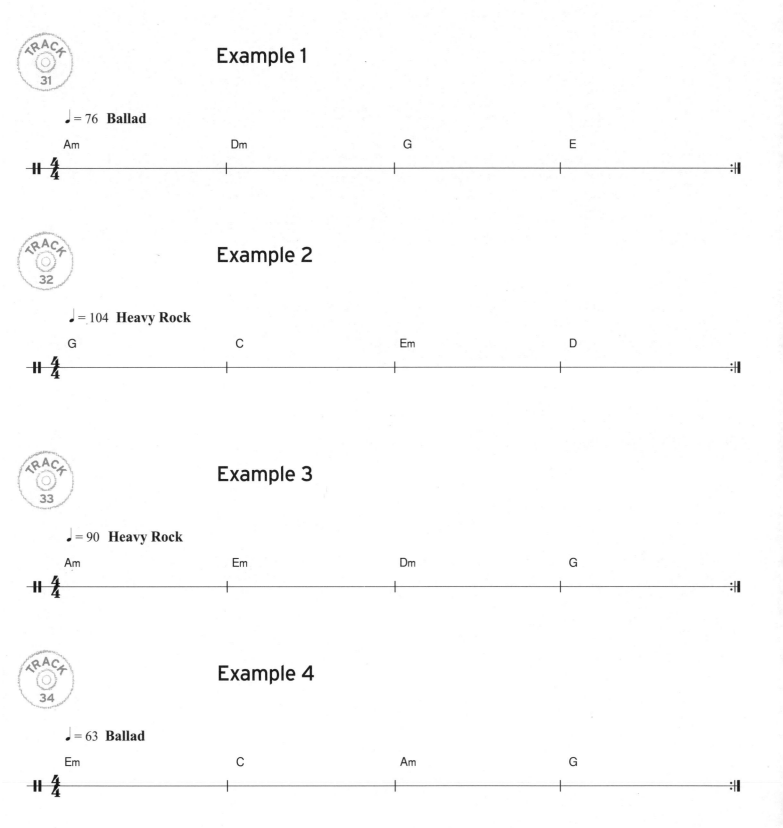

Example 1

♩ = 76 **Ballad**

| Am | Dm | G | E |

Example 2

♩ = 104 **Heavy Rock**

| G | C | Em | D |

Example 3

♩ = 90 **Heavy Rock**

| Am | Em | Dm | G |

Example 4

♩ = 63 **Ballad**

| Em | C | Am | G |

Example 5

♩ = 96 **Pop**

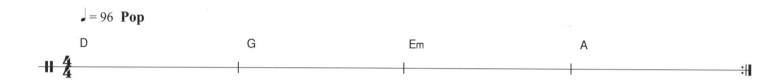

D   G   Em   A

TOP TIP The word at the top of each example describes its style. You should try to capture this in your improvisation, so listen to a range of music to become familiar with the different styles. A good way to start is by searching for different styles online.

Example 6

♩ = 100 **Heavy Rock**

C   Am   G   F

Example 7

♩ = 96 **Pop**

Em   Am   Em   B

TRACK 38

Example 8

♩ = 72 **Ballad**

| G | Am | C | D |

TRACK 39

Example 9

♩ = 88 **Heavy Rock**

| C | G | Am | F |

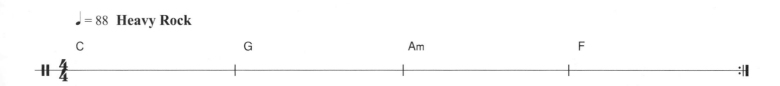

TOP TIP Listen online to other musicians improvising and think about what makes a good improvisation. Are the best improvisations complex, or can good improvising also be very simple?

TRACK 40

Example 10

♩ = 108 **Simple Rock**

| Gm | D | Gm | Cm |

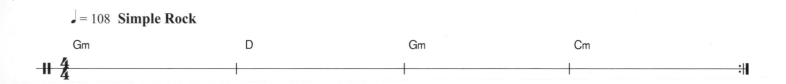

GRADE 2 PLAYBACK

Example 1

Example 2

Example 3

Example 4

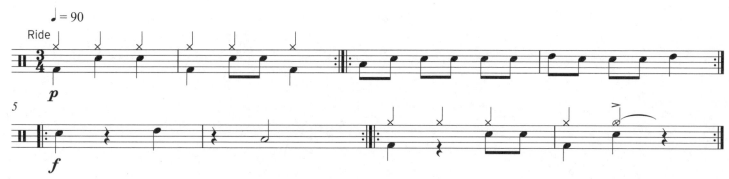

TOP TIP Notice that ties are used in playback at Grade 2. Listen carefully to the rhythms that feature ties to help you convey these when you perform them.

Example 5

Example 6

Example 7

TRACK 47

Example 8

TRACK 48

Example 9

TRACK 49

Example 10

TRACK 50

GRADE 2 IMPROVISING

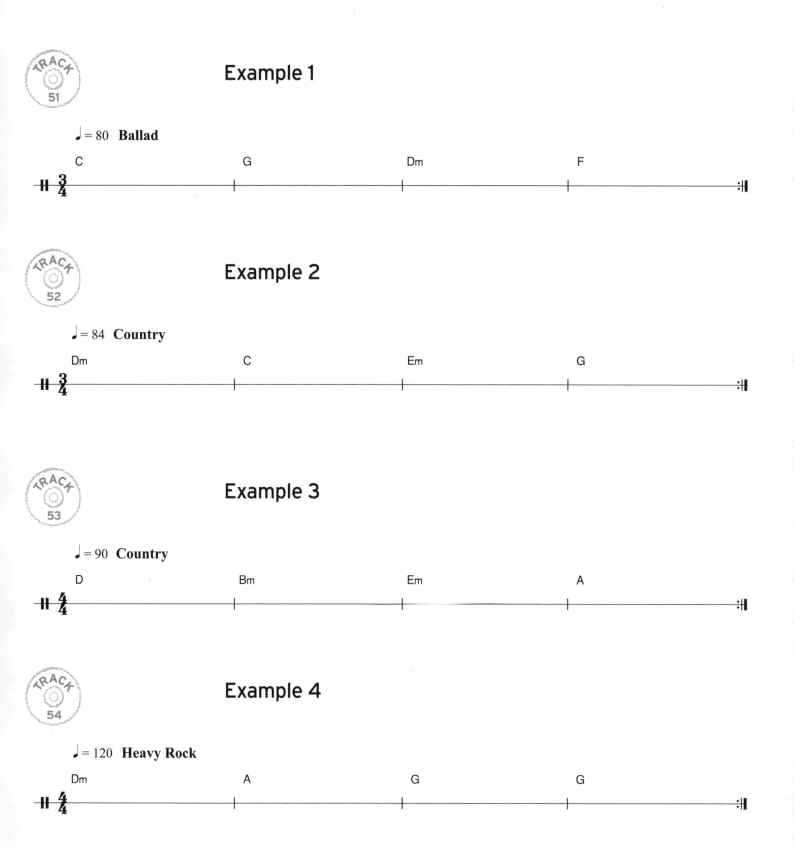

Example 1

TRACK 51

♩ = 80 **Ballad**

C   G   Dm   F

3/4

Example 2

TRACK 52

♩ = 84 **Country**

Dm   C   Em   G

3/4

Example 3

TRACK 53

♩ = 90 **Country**

D   Bm   Em   A

4/4

Example 4

TRACK 54

♩ = 120 **Heavy Rock**

Dm   A   G   G

4/4

Example 5

♩ = 96 **Simple Rock**

| F | Dm | Gm | C |

TOP TIP  The examples on this page are in very different styles. Consider what you could do in your improvising to bring out each style.

Example 6

♩ = 82 **Ballad**

| Dm | Am | G | Dm |

Example 7

♩ = 92 **Country**

| Bm | Em | G | A |

Example 8

♩ = 104 **Simple Rock**

| G | C | Em | D |

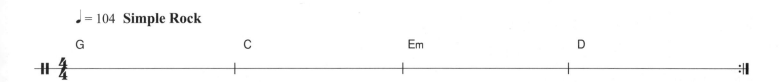

Example 9

♩ = 100 **Country**

| Dm | G | Em | A |

TOP TIP Who are your improvising heroes? Listen to as much music as you can to gain inspiration from the greats of improvisation.

Example 10

♩ = 96 **Country**

| F | C | Gm | B♭ |

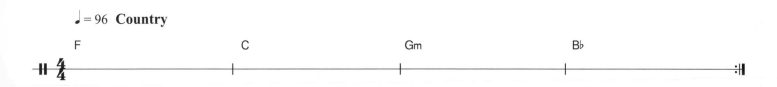

SESSION SKILLS

DRUMS NOTATION GUIDE

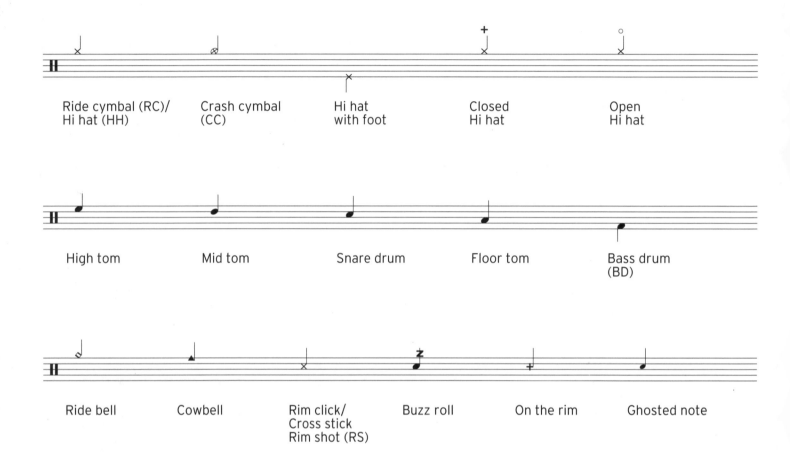

Ride cymbal (RC)/
Hi hat (HH)

Crash cymbal
(CC)

Hi hat
with foot

Closed
Hi hat

Open
Hi hat

High tom

Mid tom

Snare drum

Floor tom

Bass drum
(BD)

Ride bell

Cowbell

Rim click/
Cross stick
Rim shot (RS)

Buzz roll

On the rim

Ghosted note